Parties

My Entertainment Journal

Life is an adventure

It's not the destination we
reach that's most rewarding.
It's the journey along the way.

So **Write It Down**! & treasure
the memory forever. . .

Barbara Morina

Location: _____ Date: _____ Time: _____

Hosted by: _____

Guest(s): _____

_____

_____

_____

_____

Occasion / Theme / Event: _____

_____

Foods & Drinks: _____

_____

Music / Entertainment: _____

_____

Gifts / Party favors: _____

_____

Conversations: _____

_____

_____

_____

_____

Moments to remember: _____

_____

_____

_____

_____

Success of party / Overall feeling: _____

_____

Tips for next time: _____

_____

Parties

My Entertainment Journal

Notes: _____

_____

_____

_____

_____

_____

_____

_____

_____

_____

_____

_____

_____

Parties

My Entertainment Journal

Photos

Location: _____ . Date: _____ Time: _____

Hosted by: _____

Guest(s): _____

_____

_____

_____

_____

Occasion / Theme / Event: _____

_____

Foods & Drinks: _____

_____

Music / Entertainment: _____

_____

Gifts / Party favors: _____

_____

Conversations: _____

_____

_____

_____

_____

Moments to remember: _____

_____

_____

_____

_____

Success of party / Overall feeling: _____

_____

Tips for next time: _____

_____

_____

Notes: _____

_____

_____

_____

_____

_____

_____

_____

_____

_____

_____

_____

Parties

My Entertainment Journal

Photos

Location: _____ Date: _____ Time: _____

Hosted by: _____

Guest(s): _____

_____

_____

_____

_____

Occasion / Theme / Event: _____

_____

Foods & Drinks: _____

_____

Music / Entertainment: _____

_____

Gifts / Party favors: _____

_____

Conversations: _____

_____

_____

_____

_____

Moments to remember: _____

_____

_____

_____

_____

Success of party / Overall feeling: _____

_____

Tips for next time: _____

_____

_____

Notes: _____

_____

_____

_____

_____

_____

_____

_____

_____

_____

_____

_____

_____

_____

_____

_____

Parties

My Entertainment Journal

Photos

Location: _____. Date: _____ Time: _____

Hosted by: _____

Guest(s): _____

_____

_____

_____

Occasion / Theme / Event: _____

_____

Foods & Drinks: _____

_____

Music / Entertainment: _____

_____

Gifts / Party favors: _____

_____

Conversations: _____

_____

_____

_____

_____

Moments to remember: _____

_____

_____

_____

_____

Success of party / Overall feeling: _____

_____

Tips for next time: _____

_____

_____

Notes: _____

_____

_____

_____

_____

_____

_____

_____

_____

_____

_____

_____

_____

_____

_____

Parties

My Entertainment Journal

Photos

Location: _____ Date: _____ Time: _____

Hosted by: _____

Guest(s): _____

_____

_____

_____

_____

Occasion / Theme / Event: _____

_____

Foods & Drinks: _____

_____

Music / Entertainment: _____

_____

Gifts / Party favors: _____

_____

Conversations: _____

_____

_____

_____

_____

Moments to remember: _____

_____

_____

_____

_____

Success of party / Overall feeling: _____

_____

Tips for next time: _____

_____

Parties

My Entertainment Journal

Notes: _____

_____

_____

_____

_____

_____

_____

_____

_____

_____

_____

_____

Photos

Location: _____ . Date: _____ Time: _____

Hosted by: _____

Guest(s): _____

_____

_____

_____

_____

Occasion / Theme / Event: _____

_____

Foods & Drinks: _____

_____

Music / Entertainment: _____

_____

Gifts / Party favors: _____

_____

Conversations: _____

_____

_____

_____

_____

_____

Moments to remember: _____

_____

_____

_____

_____

_____

Success of party / Overall feeling: _____

_____

Tips for next time: _____

_____

_____

Parties

My Entertainment Journal

Notes: _____

_____

_____

_____

_____

_____

_____

_____

_____

_____

_____

_____

_____

Parties

My Entertainment Journal

Photos

Location: _____ Date: _____ Time: _____

Hosted by: _____

Guest(s): _____

_____

_____

_____

_____

Occasion / Theme / Event: _____

_____

Foods & Drinks: _____

_____

Music / Entertainment: _____

_____

Gifts / Party favors: _____

_____

Conversations: _____

_____

_____

_____

_____

Moments to remember: _____

_____

_____

_____

_____

Success of party / Overall feeling: _____

_____

Tips for next time: _____

_____

_____

© 2005 Journals Unlimited, Inc., Bay City, MI The "Write It Down"® Series

Notes: _____

_____
_____
_____
_____
_____
_____
_____
_____
_____
_____
_____
_____
_____

Photos

Location: _____ Date: _____ Time: _____

Hosted by: _____

Guest(s): _____

_____

_____

_____

Occasion / Theme / Event: _____

_____

Foods & Drinks: _____

_____

Music / Entertainment: _____

_____

Gifts / Party favors: _____

_____

Conversations: _____

_____

_____

_____

_____

Moments to remember: _____

_____

_____

_____

_____

Success of party / Overall feeling: _____

_____

Tips for next time: _____

_____

_____

Parties

My Entertainment Journal

Notes: _____

_____

_____

_____

_____

_____

_____

_____

_____

_____

_____

_____

_____

Photos

Location: _____ Date: _____ Time: _____

Hosted by: _____

Guest(s): _____

_____

_____

_____

_____

_____

Parties

My Entertainment Journal

Occasion / Theme / Event: _____

_____

Foods & Drinks: _____

_____

Music / Entertainment: _____

_____

Gifts / Party favors: _____

_____

Conversations: _____

_____

_____

_____

_____

_____

Moments to remember: _____

_____

_____

_____

_____

_____

Success of party / Overall feeling: _____

_____

Tips for next time: _____

_____

_____

Notes: _____

_____

_____

_____

_____

_____

_____

_____

_____

_____

_____

_____

_____

_____

Parties

My Entertainment Journal

Photos

Location: _____ . Date: _____ Time: _____

Hosted by: _____

Guest(s): _____

_____

_____

_____

_____

Parties

My Entertainment Journal

Occasion / Theme / Event: _____

_____

Foods & Drinks: _____

_____

Music / Entertainment: _____

_____

Gifts / Party favors: _____

_____

Conversations: _____

_____

_____

_____

_____

_____

Moments to remember: _____

_____

_____

_____

_____

Success of party / Overall feeling: _____

_____

_____

Tips for next time: _____

_____

_____

Notes: _____

_____

_____

_____

_____

_____

_____

_____

_____

_____

_____

_____

_____

Parties

My Entertainment Journal

Photos

Location: _____ Date: _____ Time: _____

Hosted by: _____

Guest(s): _____

_____

_____

_____

_____

Occasion / Theme / Event: _____

_____

Foods & Drinks: _____

_____

Music / Entertainment: _____

_____

Gifts / Party favors: _____

_____

Conversations: _____

_____

_____

_____

_____

Moments to remember: _____

_____

_____

_____

_____

Success of party / Overall feeling: _____

_____

Tips for next time: _____

_____

_____

Parties

My Entertainment Journal

Notes: _____

_____

_____

_____

_____

_____

_____

_____

_____

_____

_____

_____

_____

_____

Parties

My Entertainment Journal

Photos

Location: _____ Date: _____ Time: _____

Hosted by: _____

Guest(s): _____

_____

_____

_____

_____

Occasion / Theme / Event: _____

_____

Foods & Drinks: _____

_____

Music / Entertainment: _____

_____

Gifts / Party favors: _____

_____

Conversations: _____

_____

_____

_____

_____

Moments to remember: _____

_____

_____

_____

_____

Success of party / Overall feeling: _____

_____

Tips for next time: _____

_____

_____

Parties

My Entertainment Journal

Notes: _____

_____

_____

_____

_____

_____

_____

_____

_____

_____

_____

_____

_____

Parties

My Entertainment Journal

Photos

Location: _____ Date: _____ Time: _____

Hosted by: _____

Guest(s): _____

_____

_____

_____

_____

Parties

My Entertainment Journal

Occasion / Theme / Event: _____

_____

Foods & Drinks: _____

_____

Music / Entertainment: _____

_____

Gifts / Party favors: _____

_____

Conversations: _____

_____

_____

_____

_____

_____

Moments to remember: _____

_____

_____

_____

_____

Success of party / Overall feeling: _____

_____

Tips for next time: _____

_____

_____

Notes: _____

Parties
My Entertainment Journal

_____
_____
_____
_____
_____
_____
_____
_____
_____
_____
_____
_____
_____
_____

Photos

Location:_____. Date:_____ Time:_____

Hosted by:_____

Guest(s):_____

_____

_____

_____

_____

Occasion / Theme / Event:_____

_____

Foods & Drinks:_____

_____

Music / Entertainment:_____

_____

Gifts / Party favors:_____

_____

Conversations:_____

_____

_____

_____

_____

Moments to remember:_____

_____

_____

_____

_____

Success of party / Overall feeling:_____

_____

Tips for next time:_____

_____

_____

Notes: _____

_____

_____

_____

_____

_____

_____

_____

_____

_____

_____

_____

_____

_____

Parties

My Entertainment Journal

Photos

Location: _____ . Date: _____ Time: _____

Hosted by: _____

Guest(s): _____

_____

_____

_____

_____

Occasion / Theme / Event: _____

_____

Foods & Drinks: _____

_____

Music / Entertainment: _____

_____

Gifts / Party favors: _____

_____

Conversations: _____

_____

_____

_____

_____

Moments to remember: _____

_____

_____

_____

_____

Success of party / Overall feeling: _____

_____

Tips for next time: _____

_____

_____

Parties
My Entertainment Journal

Notes: _____

_____

_____

_____

_____

_____

_____

_____

_____

_____

_____

_____

_____

Parties

My Entertainment Journal

Photos

Location: _____. Date: _____ Time: _____

Hosted by: _____

Guest(s): _____

_____

_____

_____

_____

Occasion / Theme / Event: _____

_____

Foods & Drinks: _____

_____

Music / Entertainment: _____

_____

Gifts / Party favors: _____

_____

Conversations: _____

_____

_____

_____

_____

_____

Moments to remember: _____

_____

_____

_____

_____

Success of party / Overall feeling: _____

_____

Tips for next time: _____

_____

_____

Notes: _____

_____

_____

_____

_____

_____

_____

_____

_____

_____

_____

_____

_____

_____

_____

Photos

Location: _____ Date: _____ Time: _____

Hosted by: _____

Guest(s): _____

_____

_____

_____

Occasion / Theme / Event: _____

_____

Foods & Drinks: _____

_____

Music / Entertainment: _____

_____

Gifts / Party favors: _____

_____

Conversations: _____

_____

_____

_____

_____

Moments to remember: _____

_____

_____

_____

_____

Success of party / Overall feeling: _____

_____

Tips for next time: _____

_____

Notes: _____

_____

_____

_____

_____

_____

_____

_____

_____

_____

_____

_____

_____

_____

Parties

My Entertainment Journal

Photos

Location: _____ Date: _____ Time: _____

Hosted by: _____

Guest(s): _____

_____

_____

_____

_____

Occasion / Theme / Event: _____

_____

Foods & Drinks: _____

_____

Music / Entertainment: _____

_____

Gifts / Party favors: _____

_____

Conversations: _____

_____

_____

_____

_____

_____

Moments to remember: _____

_____

_____

_____

_____

_____

Success of party / Overall feeling: _____

_____

Tips for next time: _____

_____

_____

Notes: _____

_____

_____

_____

_____

_____

_____

_____

_____

_____

_____

_____

Photos

Location: _____ . Date: _____ Time: _____

Hosted by: _____

Guest(s): _____

_____

_____

_____

_____

Occasion / Theme / Event: _____

_____

Foods & Drinks: _____

_____

Music / Entertainment: _____

_____

Gifts / Party favors: _____

_____

Conversations: _____

_____

_____

_____

_____

_____

Moments to remember: _____

_____

_____

_____

_____

_____

Success of party / Overall feeling: _____

_____

Tips for next time: _____

_____

_____

Parties

My Entertainment Journal

Notes: _____

_____

_____

_____

_____

_____

_____

_____

_____

_____

_____

_____

_____

Photos

Location: _____ Date: _____ Time: _____

Hosted by: _____

Guest(s): _____

_____

_____

_____

_____

Occasion / Theme / Event: _____

_____

Foods & Drinks: _____

_____

Music / Entertainment: _____

_____

Gifts / Party favors: _____

_____

Conversations: _____

_____

_____

_____

_____

_____

Moments to remember: _____

_____

_____

_____

_____

Success of party / Overall feeling: _____

_____

Tips for next time: _____

_____

Notes: _____

_____

_____

_____

_____

_____

_____

_____

_____

_____

_____

_____

_____

_____

Parties

My Entertainment Journal

Photos

Location: _____ Date: _____ Time: _____

Hosted by: _____

Guest(s): _____

_____

_____

_____

_____

Occasion / Theme / Event: _____

_____

Foods & Drinks: _____

_____

Music / Entertainment: _____

_____

Gifts / Party favors: _____

_____

Conversations: _____

_____

_____

_____

_____

_____

Moments to remember: _____

_____

_____

_____

_____

Success of party / Overall feeling: _____

_____

Tips for next time: _____

_____

_____

Notes: _____

_____
_____
_____
_____
_____
_____
_____
_____
_____
_____
_____
_____
_____

Photos

Location: _____ . Date: _____ Time: _____

Hosted by: _____

Guest(s): _____

_____

_____

_____

_____

Occasion / Theme / Event: _____

_____

Foods & Drinks: _____

_____

Music / Entertainment: _____

_____

Gifts / Party favors: _____

_____

Conversations: _____

_____

_____

_____

Moments to remember: _____

_____

_____

_____

Success of party / Overall feeling: _____

_____

Tips for next time: _____

_____

_____

Parties

My Entertainment Journal

Notes: _____

_____

_____

_____

_____

_____

_____

_____

_____

_____

_____

_____

_____

_____

_____

_____

Parties

My Entertainment Journal

Photos

Location: _____ Date: _____ Time: _____

Hosted by: _____

Guest(s): _____

_____

_____

_____

_____

Occasion / Theme / Event: _____

_____

Foods & Drinks: _____

_____

Music / Entertainment: _____

_____

Gifts / Party favors: _____

_____

Conversations: _____

_____

_____

_____

_____

Moments to remember: _____

_____

_____

_____

_____

Success of party / Overall feeling: _____

_____

Tips for next time: _____

_____

_____

Notes: _____

_____

_____

_____

_____

_____

_____

_____

_____

_____

_____

_____

_____

_____

Parties

My Entertainment Journal

Photos

Location: _____ Date: _____ Time: _____

Hosted by: _____

Guest(s): _____

_____

_____

_____

_____

Occasion / Theme / Event: _____

_____

Foods & Drinks: _____

_____

Music / Entertainment: _____

_____

Gifts / Party favors: _____

_____

Conversations: _____

_____

_____

_____

_____

Moments to remember: _____

_____

_____

_____

_____

Success of party / Overall feeling: _____

_____

Tips for next time: _____

_____

_____

Notes: _____

_____

_____

_____

_____

_____

_____

_____

_____

_____

_____

_____

_____

_____

Photos

Location: _____ Date: _____ Time: _____

Hosted by: _____

Guest(s): _____

_____

_____

_____

Occasion / Theme / Event: _____

_____

Foods & Drinks: _____

_____

Music / Entertainment: _____

_____

Gifts / Party favors: _____

_____

Conversations: _____

_____

_____

_____

_____

Moments to remember: _____

_____

_____

_____

_____

Success of party / Overall feeling: _____

_____

Tips for next time: _____

_____

_____

© 2005 Journals Unlimited, Inc., Bay City, MI The "Write It Down" Series

Notes: _____

_____

_____

_____

_____

_____

_____

_____

_____

_____

_____

_____

Photos

Location: _____ . Date: _____ Time: _____

Hosted by: _____

Guest(s): _____

_____

_____

_____

_____

Occasion / Theme / Event: _____

_____

Foods & Drinks: _____

_____

Music / Entertainment: _____

_____

Gifts / Party favors: _____

_____

Conversations: _____

_____

_____

_____

_____

_____

Moments to remember: _____

_____

_____

_____

_____

Success of party / Overall feeling: _____

_____

Tips for next time: _____

_____

_____

Notes: _____

_____

_____

_____

_____

_____

_____

_____

_____

_____

_____

_____

Parties

My Entertainment Journal

Photos

Location: _____ . Date: _____ Time: _____

Hosted by: _____

Guest(s): _____

_____

_____

_____

_____

Occasion / Theme / Event: _____

_____

Foods & Drinks: _____

_____

Music / Entertainment: _____

_____

Gifts / Party favors: _____

_____

Conversations: _____

_____

_____

_____

_____

Moments to remember: _____

_____

_____

_____

_____

Success of party / Overall feeling: _____

_____

Tips for next time: _____

_____

_____

Parties
My Entertainment Journal

Notes: _____

_____

_____

_____

_____

_____

_____

_____

_____

_____

_____

_____

_____

Photos

Location: _____ . Date: _____ Time: _____

Hosted by: _____

Guest(s): _____

_____

_____

_____

_____

Occasion / Theme / Event: _____

_____

Foods & Drinks: _____

_____

Music / Entertainment: _____

_____

Gifts / Party favors: _____

_____

Conversations: _____

_____

_____

_____

_____

Moments to remember: _____

_____

_____

_____

_____

Success of party / Overall feeling: _____

_____

Tips for next time: _____

_____

_____

Parties

My Entertainment Journal

Notes: _____

_____

_____

_____

_____

_____

_____

_____

_____

_____

_____

_____

_____

Parties

My Entertainment Journal

Photos

Location: _____ Date: _____ Time: _____

Hosted by: _____

Guest(s): _____

_____

_____

_____

_____

Occasion / Theme / Event: _____

_____

Foods & Drinks: _____

_____

Music / Entertainment: _____

_____

Gifts / Party favors: _____

_____

Conversations: _____

_____

_____

_____

_____

Moments to remember: _____

_____

_____

_____

_____

Success of party / Overall feeling: _____

_____

Tips for next time: _____

_____

_____

Notes: _____

_____

_____

_____

_____

_____

_____

_____

_____

_____

_____

_____

_____

Parties

My Entertainment Journal

Photos

Location: _____ . Date: _____ Time: _____

Hosted by: _____

Guest(s): _____

_____

_____

_____

_____

Occasion / Theme / Event: _____

_____

Foods & Drinks: _____

_____

Music / Entertainment: _____

_____

Gifts / Party favors: _____

_____

Conversations: _____

_____

_____

_____

_____

_____

Moments to remember: _____

_____

_____

_____

_____

Success of party / Overall feeling: _____

_____

Tips for next time: _____

_____

_____

Parties

My Entertainment Journal

Notes: _____

_____

_____

_____

_____

_____

_____

_____

_____

_____

_____

_____

_____

_____

Parties

My Entertainment Journal

Photos

Location: _____ . Date: _____ Time: _____

Hosted by: _____

Guest(s): _____

_____

_____

_____

_____

Occasion / Theme / Event: _____

_____

Foods & Drinks: _____

_____

Music / Entertainment: _____

_____

Gifts / Party favors: _____

_____

Conversations: _____

_____

_____

_____

_____

_____

Moments to remember: _____

_____

_____

_____

_____

Success of party / Overall feeling: _____

_____

Tips for next time: _____

_____

_____

Notes: _____

_____

_____

_____

_____

_____

_____

_____

_____

_____

_____

_____

_____

_____

Photos

Location: _____ Date: _____ Time: _____

Hosted by: _____

Guest(s): _____

_____

_____

_____

_____

Occasion / Theme / Event: _____

_____

Foods & Drinks: _____

_____

Music / Entertainment: _____

_____

Gifts / Party favors: _____

_____

Conversations: _____

_____

_____

_____

_____

Moments to remember: _____

_____

_____

_____

_____

Success of party / Overall feeling: _____

_____

Tips for next time: _____

_____

_____

Parties

My Entertainment Journal

Notes: _____

_____

_____

_____

_____

_____

_____

_____

_____

_____

_____

_____

_____

_____

Parties

My Entertainment Journal

Photos

Location: _____ Date: _____ Time: _____

Hosted by: _____

Guest(s): _____

_____

_____

_____

_____

Occasion / Theme / Event: _____

_____

Foods & Drinks: _____

_____

Music / Entertainment: _____

_____

Gifts / Party favors: _____

_____

Conversations: _____

_____

_____

_____

_____

Moments to remember: _____

_____

_____

_____

_____

Success of party / Overall feeling: _____

_____

Tips for next time: _____

_____

_____

Notes: _____ ___

_____

_____

_____

_____

_____

_____

_____

_____

_____

_____

_____

_____

Parties

My Entertainment Journal

Photos

Location: _____ Date: _____ Time: _____

Hosted by: _____

Guest(s): _____

_____

_____

_____

_____

Parties

My Entertainment Journal

Occasion / Theme / Event: _____

_____

Foods & Drinks: _____

_____

Music / Entertainment: _____

_____

Gifts / Party favors: _____

_____

Conversations: _____

_____

_____

_____

_____

_____

Moments to remember: _____

_____

_____

_____

_____

_____

Success of party / Overall feeling: _____

_____

Tips for next time: _____

_____

Notes: _____

_____

_____

_____

_____

_____

_____

_____

_____

_____

_____

_____

_____

Photos

Location: _____ . Date: _____ Time: _____

Hosted by: _____

Guest(s): _____

_____

_____

_____

_____

_____

Occasion / Theme / Event: _____

_____

Foods & Drinks: _____

_____

Music / Entertainment: _____

_____

Gifts / Party favors: _____

_____

Conversations: _____

_____

_____

_____

_____

_____

Moments to remember: _____

_____

_____

_____

_____

_____

Success of party / Overall feeling: _____

_____

Tips for next time: _____

_____

_____

Parties

My Entertainment Journal

Notes: _____

_____

_____

_____

_____

_____

_____

_____

_____

_____

_____

_____

_____

Parties

My Entertainment Journal

Photos

Location: _____ . Date: _____ Time: _____

Hosted by: _____

Guest(s): _____

_____

_____

_____

_____

Occasion / Theme / Event: _____

_____

Foods & Drinks: _____

_____

Music / Entertainment: _____

_____

Gifts / Party favors: _____

_____

Conversations: _____

_____

_____

_____

_____

Moments to remember: _____

_____

_____

_____

_____

Success of party / Overall feeling: _____

_____

Tips for next time: _____

_____

_____

Parties

My Entertainment Journal

Notes: _____

_____

_____

_____

_____

_____

_____

_____

_____

_____

_____

_____

_____

_____

Parties
My Entertainment Journal

Photos

Location: _____ Date: _____ Time: _____

Hosted by: _____

Guest(s): _____

_____

_____

_____

_____

Occasion / Theme / Event: _____

_____

Foods & Drinks: _____

_____

Music / Entertainment: _____

_____

Gifts / Party favors: _____

_____

Conversations: _____

_____

_____

_____

_____

Moments to remember: _____

_____

_____

_____

_____

Success of party / Overall feeling: _____

_____

Tips for next time: _____

_____

_____

Parties

My Entertainment Journal

Notes: _____

_____
_____
_____
_____
_____
_____
_____
_____
_____
_____
_____
_____
_____
_____

Photos

Location: _____ . Date: _____ Time: _____

Hosted by: _____

Guest(s): _____

_____

_____

_____

_____

Occasion / Theme / Event: _____

_____

Foods & Drinks: _____

_____

Music / Entertainment: _____

_____

Gifts / Party favors: _____

_____

Conversations: _____

_____

_____

_____

_____

_____

Moments to remember: _____

_____

_____

_____

_____

_____

Success of party / Overall feeling: _____

_____

Tips for next time: _____

_____

_____

Parties

My Entertainment Journal

Notes: _____

_____

_____

_____

_____

_____

_____

_____

_____

_____

_____

_____

_____

_____

Photos

Location: _____ . Date: _____ Time: _____

Hosted by: _____

Guest(s): _____

_____

_____

_____

_____

Occasion / Theme / Event: _____

_____

Foods & Drinks: _____

_____

Music / Entertainment: _____

_____

Gifts / Party favors: _____

_____

Conversations: _____

_____

_____

_____

_____

_____

Moments to remember: _____

_____

_____

_____

_____

_____

Success of party / Overall feeling: _____

_____

Tips for next time: _____

_____

_____

Parties

My Entertainment Journal

Notes: _____

_____

_____

_____

_____

_____

_____

_____

_____

_____

_____

_____

Parties
My Entertainment Journal

Photos

Location: _____ . Date: _____ Time: _____

Hosted by: _____

Guest(s): _____

_____

_____

_____

_____

Occasion / Theme / Event: _____

_____

Foods & Drinks: _____

_____

Music / Entertainment: _____

_____

Gifts / Party favors: _____

_____

Conversations: _____

_____

_____

_____

_____

Moments to remember: _____

_____

_____

_____

_____

Success of party / Overall feeling: _____

_____

Tips for next time: _____

_____

_____

Notes: _____

_____

_____

_____

_____

_____

_____

_____

_____

_____

_____

_____

_____

_____

Parties

My Entertainment Journal

Photos

Location: _____ . Date: _____ Time: _____

Hosted by: _____

Guest(s): _____

_____

_____

_____

_____

Occasion / Theme / Event: _____

_____

Foods & Drinks: _____

_____

Music / Entertainment: _____

_____

Gifts / Party favors: _____

_____

Conversations: _____

_____

_____

_____

_____

Moments to remember: _____

_____

_____

_____

_____

Success of party / Overall feeling: _____

_____

Tips for next time: _____

_____

_____

Notes: _____

_____

_____

_____

_____

_____

_____

_____

_____

_____

_____

_____

_____

_____

_____

Parties

My Entertainment Journal

Photos

Location: _____ . Date: _____ Time: _____

Hosted by: _____

Guest(s): _____

_____

_____

_____

Occasion / Theme / Event: _____

_____

Foods & Drinks: _____

_____

Music / Entertainment: _____

_____

Gifts / Party favors: _____

_____

Conversations: _____

_____

_____

_____

_____

Moments to remember: _____

_____

_____

_____

_____

Success of party / Overall feeling: _____

_____

Tips for next time: _____

_____

Notes: _____

Parties

My Entertainment Journal

_____
_____
_____
_____
_____
_____
_____
_____
_____
_____
_____
_____
_____
_____
_____
_____

Photos

Location: _____ . Date: _____ Time: _____

Hosted by: _____

Guest(s): _____

_____

_____

_____

_____

Occasion / Theme / Event: _____

_____

Foods & Drinks: _____

_____

Music / Entertainment: _____

_____

Gifts / Party favors: _____

_____

Conversations: _____

_____

_____

_____

_____

Moments to remember: _____

_____

_____

_____

_____

Success of party / Overall feeling: _____

_____

Tips for next time: _____

_____

_____

Parties

My Entertainment Journal

Notes: _____

_____

_____

_____

_____

_____

_____

_____

_____

_____

_____

_____

_____

Photos

Location: _____ Date: _____ Time: _____

Hosted by: _____

Guest(s): _____

_____

_____

_____

_____

Occasion / Theme / Event: _____

_____

Foods & Drinks: _____

_____

Music / Entertainment: _____

_____

Gifts / Party favors: _____

_____

Conversations: _____

_____

_____

_____

_____

Moments to remember: _____

_____

_____

_____

_____

Success of party / Overall feeling: _____

_____

Tips for next time: _____

_____

_____

Notes: _____

_____

_____

_____

_____

_____

_____

_____

_____

_____

_____

_____

Parties

My Entertainment Journal

Photos

Location: _____ . Date: _____ Time: _____

Hosted by: _____

Guest(s): _____

_____

_____

_____

_____

Occasion / Theme / Event: _____

_____

Foods & Drinks: _____

_____

Music / Entertainment: _____

_____

Gifts / Party favors: _____

_____

Conversations: _____

_____

_____

_____

_____

Moments to remember: _____

_____

_____

_____

_____

Success of party / Overall feeling: _____

_____

Tips for next time: _____

_____

Parties

My Entertainment Journal

Parties

My Entertainment Journal

Photos

Location: _____ . Date: _____ Time: _____

Hosted by: _____

Guest(s): _____

_____

_____

_____

_____

Occasion / Theme / Event: _____

_____

Foods & Drinks: _____

_____

Music / Entertainment: _____

_____

Gifts / Party favors: _____

_____

Conversations: _____

_____

_____

_____

_____

Moments to remember: _____

_____

_____

_____

_____

Success of party / Overall feeling: _____

_____

Tips for next time: _____

_____

_____

© 2005 Journals Unlimited, Inc., Bay City, MI   The *"Write It Down"* ® Series

Parties

My Entertainment Journal

Notes: _____

_____

_____

_____

_____

_____

_____

_____

_____

_____

_____

Parties

My Entertainment Journal

Photos

Location: _____ . Date: _____ Time: _____

Hosted by: _____

Guest(s): _____

_____

_____

_____

_____

Occasion / Theme / Event: _____

_____

Foods & Drinks: _____

_____

Music / Entertainment: _____

_____

Gifts / Party favors: _____

_____

Conversations: _____

_____

_____

_____

_____

Moments to remember: _____

_____

_____

_____

_____

Success of party / Overall feeling: _____

_____

Tips for next time: _____

_____

Notes: _____

_____

_____

_____

_____

_____

_____

_____

_____

_____

_____

_____

_____

Photos

Location: _____ . Date: _____ Time: _____

Hosted by: _____

Guest(s): _____

_____

_____

_____

_____

Occasion / Theme / Event: _____

_____

Foods & Drinks: _____

_____

Music / Entertainment: _____

_____

Gifts / Party favors: _____

_____

Conversations: _____

_____

_____

_____

_____

Moments to remember: _____

_____

_____

_____

_____

Success of party / Overall feeling: _____

_____

Tips for next time: _____

_____

_____

Notes: _____

_____

_____

_____

_____

_____

_____

_____

_____

_____

_____

_____

_____

_____

Parties

My Entertainment Journal

Photos

Location: _____ . Date: _____ Time: _____

Hosted by: _____

Guest(s): _____

_____

_____

_____

_____

Occasion / Theme / Event: _____

_____

Foods & Drinks: _____

_____

Music / Entertainment: _____

_____

Gifts / Party favors: _____

_____

Conversations: _____

_____

_____

_____

_____

Moments to remember: _____

_____

_____

_____

_____

Success of party / Overall feeling: _____

_____

Tips for next time: _____

_____

_____

Parties

My Entertainment Journal

Notes: _____

_____

_____

_____

_____

_____

_____

_____

_____

_____

_____

_____

_____

Parties

My Entertainment Journal

Photos

Location: _____ . Date: _____ Time: _____

Hosted by: _____

Guest(s): _____

_____

_____

_____

Occasion / Theme / Event: _____

_____

Foods & Drinks: _____

_____

Music / Entertainment: _____

_____

Gifts / Party favors: _____

_____

Conversations: _____

_____

_____

_____

_____

Moments to remember: _____

_____

_____

_____

_____

Success of party / Overall feeling: _____

_____

Tips for next time: _____

_____

_____

Parties

My Entertainment Journal

Notes: _____

_____

_____

_____

_____

_____

_____

_____

_____

_____

_____

_____

_____

_____

Parties

My Entertainment Journal

Photos

Location: _____ . Date: _____ Time: _____

Hosted by: _____

Guest(s): _____

_____

_____

_____

_____

Occasion / Theme / Event: _____

_____

Foods & Drinks: _____

_____

Music / Entertainment: _____

_____

Gifts / Party favors: _____

_____

Conversations: _____

_____

_____

_____

_____

_____

Moments to remember: _____

_____

_____

_____

_____

Success of party / Overall feeling: _____

_____

Tips for next time: _____

_____

Notes: _____

_____

Parties

My Entertainment Journal

_____

_____

_____

_____

_____

_____

_____

_____

_____

_____

Photos

Location: _____ . Date: _____ Time: _____

Hosted by: _____

Guest(s): _____

_____

_____

_____

_____

Occasion / Theme / Event: _____

_____

Foods & Drinks: _____

_____

Music / Entertainment: _____

_____

Gifts / Party favors: _____

_____

Conversations: _____

_____

_____

_____

_____

Moments to remember: _____

_____

_____

_____

_____

Success of party / Overall feeling: _____

_____

Tips for next time: _____

_____

Parties

My Entertainment Journal

Notes: _____

_____

_____

_____

_____

_____

_____

_____

_____

_____

_____

_____

_____

Parties

My Entertainment Journal

Photos

Location: _____ Date: _____ Time: _____

Parties

Hosted by: _____

Guest(s): _____

_____

_____

My Entertainment Journal

_____

_____

Occasion / Theme / Event: _____

_____

Foods & Drinks: _____

_____

Music / Entertainment: _____

_____

Gifts / Party favors: _____

_____

Conversations: _____

_____

_____

_____

_____

Moments to remember: _____

_____

_____

_____

_____

Success of party / Overall feeling: _____

_____

Tips for next time: _____

_____

_____

Notes: _____

_____

_____

_____

_____

_____

_____

_____

_____

_____

_____

_____

_____

Parties

My Entertainment Journal

Photos

Location: _____. Date: _____ Time: _____

Hosted by: _____

Guest(s): _____

_____

_____

_____

Occasion / Theme / Event: _____

_____

Foods & Drinks: _____

_____

Music / Entertainment: _____

_____

Gifts / Party favors: _____

_____

Conversations: _____

_____

_____

_____

_____

Moments to remember: _____

_____

_____

_____

_____

Success of party / Overall feeling: _____

_____

Tips for next time: _____

_____

_____

Notes: _____

_____

_____

_____

_____

_____

_____

_____

_____

_____

_____

_____

_____

_____

_____

_____

Parties

My Entertainment Journal

Photos

Location: _____ Date: _____ Time: _____

Hosted by: _____

Guest(s): _____

_____

_____

_____

_____

Occasion / Theme / Event: _____

_____

Foods & Drinks: _____

_____

Music / Entertainment: _____

_____

Gifts / Party favors: _____

_____

Conversations: _____

_____

_____

_____

_____

Moments to remember: _____

_____

_____

_____

_____

Success of party / Overall feeling: _____

_____

Tips for next time: _____

_____

_____

Parties

My Entertainment Journal

Notes: _____

_____

_____

_____

_____

_____

_____

_____

_____

_____

_____

_____

_____

Parties

My Entertainment Journal

Photos

Location: _____ . Date: _____ Time: _____

Hosted by: _____

Guest(s): _____

_____

_____

_____

_____

Occasion / Theme / Event: _____

_____

Foods & Drinks: _____

_____

Music / Entertainment: _____

_____

Gifts / Party favors: _____

_____

Conversations: _____

_____

_____

_____

_____

Moments to remember: _____

_____

_____

_____

_____

Success of party / Overall feeling: _____

_____

Tips for next time: _____

_____

Parties

My Entertainment Journal

Notes: _____

_____

_____

_____

_____

_____

_____

_____

_____

_____

_____

_____

_____

_____

Parties

My Entertainment Journal

Photos

Location: _____ . Date: _____ Time: _____

Hosted by: _____

Guest(s): _____

_____

_____

_____

_____

Occasion / Theme / Event: _____

_____

Foods & Drinks: _____

_____

Music / Entertainment: _____

_____

Gifts / Party favors: _____

_____

Conversations: _____

_____

_____

_____

_____

Moments to remember: _____

_____

_____

_____

_____

Success of party / Overall feeling: _____

_____

Tips for next time: _____

_____

_____

Parties

My Entertainment Journal

Parties
My Entertainment Journal

Photos

Location: _____ . Date: _____ Time: _____

Hosted by: _____

Guest(s): _____

_____

_____

_____

_____

Occasion / Theme / Event: _____

_____

Foods & Drinks: _____

_____

Music / Entertainment: _____

_____

Gifts / Party favors: _____

_____

Conversations: _____

_____

_____

_____

_____

Moments to remember: _____

_____

_____

_____

Success of party / Overall feeling: _____

_____

Tips for next time: _____

_____

_____

Parties

My Entertainment Journal

Notes: _____

_____

_____

_____

_____

_____

_____

_____

_____

_____

_____

_____

_____

_____

Photos

Location: _____ Date: _____ Time: _____

Hosted by: _____

Guest(s): _____

_____

_____

_____

Occasion / Theme / Event: _____

_____

Foods & Drinks: _____

_____

Music / Entertainment: _____

_____

Gifts / Party favors: _____

_____

Conversations: _____

_____

_____

_____

_____

Moments to remember: _____

_____

_____

_____

_____

Success of party / Overall feeling: _____

_____

Tips for next time: _____

_____

_____

Parties
My Entertainment Journal

Notes: _____

_____

_____

_____

_____

_____

_____

_____

_____

_____

_____

_____

Parties

My Entertainment Journal

Photos

Location: _____ . Date: _____ Time: _____

Hosted by: _____

Guest(s): _____

_____

_____

_____

_____

Occasion / Theme / Event: _____

_____

Foods & Drinks: _____

_____

Music / Entertainment: _____

_____

Gifts / Party favors: _____

_____

Conversations: _____

_____

_____

_____

_____

_____

Moments to remember: _____

_____

_____

_____

_____

_____

Success of party / Overall feeling: _____

_____

Tips for next time: _____

_____

_____

Notes: _____

_____

_____

_____

_____

_____

_____

_____

_____

_____

_____

_____

Photos

Location: _____ . Date: _____ Time: _____

Hosted by: _____

Guest(s): _____

_____

_____

_____

_____

Occasion / Theme / Event: _____

_____

Foods & Drinks: _____

_____

Music / Entertainment: _____

_____

Gifts / Party favors: _____

_____

Conversations: _____

_____

_____

_____

_____

Moments to remember: _____

_____

_____

_____

_____

Success of party / Overall feeling: _____

_____

_____

Tips for next time: _____

_____

_____

Parties

My Entertainment Journal

Notes: _____

Parties
My Entertainment Journal

_____
_____
_____
_____
_____
_____
_____
_____
_____
_____
_____
_____
_____

Photos

Location: _____ . Date: _____ Time: _____

Hosted by: _____

Guest(s): _____

_____

_____

_____

_____

Occasion / Theme / Event: _____

_____

Foods & Drinks: _____

_____

Music / Entertainment: _____

_____

Gifts / Party favors: _____

_____

Conversations: _____

_____

_____

_____

_____

Moments to remember: _____

_____

_____

_____

_____

Success of party / Overall feeling: _____

_____

Tips for next time: _____

_____

_____

Notes: _____

Parties

My Entertainment Journal

_____

_____

_____

_____

_____

_____

_____

_____

_____

_____

_____

_____

Photos

Location: _____ . Date: _____ Time: _____

Hosted by: _____

Guest(s): _____

_____

_____

_____

_____

Occasion / Theme / Event: _____

_____

Foods & Drinks: _____

_____

Music / Entertainment: _____

_____

Gifts / Party favors: _____

_____

Conversations: _____

_____

_____

_____

_____

Moments to remember: _____

_____

_____

_____

_____

Success of party / Overall feeling: _____

_____

Tips for next time: _____

_____

_____

Notes: _____

_____

_____

_____

_____

_____

_____

_____

_____

_____

_____

_____

_____

_____

_____

_____

Photos

Location: _____ . Date: _____ Time: _____

Hosted by: _____

Guest(s): _____

_____

_____

_____

_____

Occasion / Theme / Event: _____

_____

Foods & Drinks: _____

_____

Music / Entertainment: _____

_____

Gifts / Party favors: _____

_____

Conversations: _____

_____

_____

_____

_____

Moments to remember: _____

_____

_____

_____

_____

Success of party / Overall feeling: _____

_____

Tips for next time: _____

_____

Notes: _____

_____

_____

_____

_____

_____

_____

_____

_____

_____

_____

_____

_____

_____

Parties

My Entertainment Journal

Photos

Location: _____. Date: _____ Time: _____

Hosted by: _____

Guest(s): _____

_____

_____

_____

_____

Occasion / Theme / Event: _____

_____

Foods & Drinks: _____

_____

Music / Entertainment: _____

_____

Gifts / Party favors: _____

_____

Conversations: _____

_____

_____

_____

_____

Moments to remember: _____

_____

_____

_____

_____

Success of party / Overall feeling: _____

_____

Tips for next time: _____

_____

_____

 The "Write It Down"® Series

Parties

My Entertainment Journal

Notes: _____

_____

_____

_____

_____

_____

_____

_____

_____

_____

_____

_____

_____

Photos

Location: _____ . Date: _____ Time: _____

Hosted by: _____

Guest(s): _____

_____

_____

_____

_____

Occasion / Theme / Event: _____

_____

Foods & Drinks: _____

_____

Music / Entertainment: _____

_____

Gifts / Party favors: _____

_____

Conversations: _____

_____

_____

_____

_____

Moments to remember: _____

_____

_____

_____

_____

Success of party / Overall feeling: _____

_____

Tips for next time: _____

_____

_____

Notes: _____

_____

_____

_____

_____

_____

_____

_____

_____

_____

_____

_____

_____

_____

Photos

Location: _____. Date: _____ Time: _____

Hosted by: _____

Guest(s): _____

_____

_____

_____

Occasion / Theme / Event: _____

_____

Foods & Drinks: _____

_____

Music / Entertainment: _____

_____

Gifts / Party favors: _____

_____

Conversations: _____

_____

_____

_____

_____

Moments to remember: _____

_____

_____

_____

Success of party / Overall feeling: _____

_____

Tips for next time: _____

_____

_____

Notes: _____

_____

_____

_____

_____

_____

_____

_____

_____

_____

_____

_____

_____

_____

Parties

My Entertainment Journal

Photos

Location: _____ . Date: _____ Time: _____

Hosted by: _____

Guest(s): _____

_____

_____

_____

_____

Occasion / Theme / Event: _____

_____

Foods & Drinks: _____

_____

Music / Entertainment: _____

_____

Gifts / Party favors: _____

_____

Conversations: _____

_____

_____

_____

_____

Moments to remember: _____

_____

_____

_____

_____

Success of party / Overall feeling: _____

_____

Tips for next time: _____

_____

_____

Parties

My Entertainment Journal

Notes: _____

_____

_____

_____

_____

_____

_____

_____

_____

_____

_____

_____

_____

_____

_____

Photos

Location: _____ . Date: _____ Time: _____

Hosted by: _____

Guest(s): _____

_____

_____

_____

Occasion / Theme / Event: _____

_____

Foods & Drinks: _____

_____

Music / Entertainment: _____

_____

Gifts / Party favors: _____

_____

Conversations: _____

_____

_____

_____

_____

Moments to remember: _____

_____

_____

_____

Success of party / Overall feeling: _____

_____

Tips for next time: _____

_____

_____

Parties

My Entertainment Journal

Notes: _____

_____

_____

_____

_____

_____

_____

_____

_____

_____

_____

_____

_____

Parties

My Entertainment Journal

Photos

Location: _____ . Date: _____ Time: _____

Hosted by: _____

Guest(s): _____

_____

_____

_____

_____

Occasion / Theme / Event: _____

_____

Foods & Drinks: _____

_____

Music / Entertainment: _____

_____

Gifts / Party favors: _____

_____

Conversations: _____

_____

_____

_____

_____

Moments to remember: _____

_____

_____

_____

_____

Success of party / Overall feeling: _____

_____

Tips for next time: _____

_____

_____

Parties

My Entertainment Journal

Notes: _____

_____

_____

_____

_____

_____

_____

_____

_____

_____

_____

_____

Photos

Location: _____ . Date: _____ Time: _____

Hosted by: _____

Guest(s): _____

_____

_____

_____

Occasion / Theme / Event: _____

_____

Foods & Drinks: _____

_____

Music / Entertainment: _____

_____

Gifts / Party favors: _____

_____

Conversations: _____

_____

_____

_____

_____

Moments to remember: _____

_____

_____

_____

_____

Success of party / Overall feeling: _____

_____

Tips for next time: _____

_____

_____

© 2005 Journals Unlimited, Inc., Bay City, MI The "Write It Down" Series

Parties

My Entertainment Journal

Notes: _____

_____

_____

_____

_____

_____

_____

_____

_____

_____

_____

_____

Parties

My Entertainment Journal

Photos

Location: _____ . Date: _____ Time: _____

Hosted by: _____

Guest(s): _____

_____

_____

_____

_____

Occasion / Theme / Event: _____

_____

Foods & Drinks: _____

_____

Music / Entertainment: _____

_____

Gifts / Party favors: _____

_____

Conversations: _____

_____

_____

_____

_____

Moments to remember: _____

_____

_____

_____

Success of party / Overall feeling: _____

_____

Tips for next time: _____

_____

_____

Parties

My Entertainment Journal

Notes: _____

_____

_____

_____

_____

_____

_____

_____

_____

_____

_____

_____

_____

Parties

My Entertainment Journal

Photos

Location: _____ . Date: _____ Time: _____

Hosted by: _____

Guest(s): _____

_____

_____

_____

_____

Occasion / Theme / Event: _____

_____

Foods & Drinks: _____

_____

Music / Entertainment: _____

_____

Gifts / Party favors: _____

_____

Conversations: _____

_____

_____

_____

_____

Moments to remember: _____

_____

_____

_____

_____

Success of party / Overall feeling: _____

_____

Tips for next time: _____

_____

_____

Parties

My Entertainment Journal

Notes:

Photos

Location: _____. Date: _____ Time: _____

Hosted by: _____

Guest(s): _____

_____

_____

_____

_____

Occasion / Theme / Event: _____

_____

Foods & Drinks: _____

_____

Music / Entertainment: _____

_____

Gifts / Party favors: _____

_____

Conversations: _____

_____

_____

_____

_____

Moments to remember: _____

_____

_____

_____

_____

Success of party / Overall feeling: _____

_____

Tips for next time: _____

_____

_____

© 2005 Journals Unlimited, Inc., Bay City, MI   The "Write It Down"® Series

Parties

My Entertainment Journal

Notes: _____

_____

_____

_____

_____

_____

_____

_____

_____

_____

_____

_____

Parties

My Entertainment Journal

Photos

Location: _____ . Date: _____ Time: _____

Hosted by: _____

Guest(s): _____

_____

_____

_____

_____

_____

Occasion / Theme / Event: _____

_____

Foods & Drinks: _____

_____

Music / Entertainment: _____

_____

Gifts / Party favors: _____

_____

Conversations: _____

_____

_____

_____

_____

Moments to remember: _____

_____

_____

_____

_____

Success of party / Overall feeling: _____

_____

Tips for next time: _____

_____

_____

Notes: _____

Parties
My Entertainment Journal

_____
_____
_____
_____
_____
_____
_____
_____
_____
_____
_____
_____
_____
_____
_____

Photos

Location: _____ Date: _____ Time: _____

Hosted by: _____

Guest(s): _____

_____

_____

_____

_____

Occasion / Theme / Event: _____

_____

Foods & Drinks: _____

_____

Music / Entertainment: _____

_____

Gifts / Party favors: _____

_____

Conversations: _____

_____

_____

_____

_____

Moments to remember: _____

_____

_____

_____

_____

Success of party / Overall feeling: _____

_____

Tips for next time: _____

_____

_____

Notes: _____

_____

_____

_____

_____

_____

_____

_____

_____

_____

_____

_____

_____

_____

Parties

My Entertainment Journal

Photos

Location: _____ . Date: _____ Time: _____

Hosted by: _____

Guest(s): _____

_____

_____

_____

_____

Occasion / Theme / Event: _____

_____

Foods & Drinks: _____

_____

Music / Entertainment: _____

_____

Gifts / Party favors: _____

_____

Conversations: _____

_____

_____

_____

_____

Moments to remember: _____

_____

_____

_____

_____

Success of party / Overall feeling: _____

_____

Tips for next time: _____

_____

_____

Parties

My Entertainment Journal

Notes: _____

_____

_____

_____

_____

_____

_____

_____

_____

_____

_____

_____

_____

_____

_____

Parties

My Entertainment Journal

Photos

Location: _____ . Date: _____ Time: _____

Hosted by: _____

Guest(s): _____

_____

_____

_____

_____

Occasion / Theme / Event: _____

_____

Foods & Drinks: _____

_____

Music / Entertainment: _____

_____

Gifts / Party favors: _____

_____

Conversations: _____

_____

_____

_____

_____

_____

Moments to remember: _____

_____

_____

_____

_____

Success of party / Overall feeling: _____

_____

Tips for next time: _____

_____

_____

Parties

My Entertainment Journal

Notes: _____

_____

_____

_____

_____

_____

_____

_____

_____

_____

_____

_____

Parties

My Entertainment Journal

Photos

Location: _____ Date: _____ Time: _____

Hosted by: _____

Guest(s): _____

_____

_____

_____

_____

Occasion / Theme / Event: _____

_____

Foods & Drinks: _____

_____

Music / Entertainment: _____

_____

Gifts / Party favors: _____

_____

Conversations: _____

_____

_____

_____

_____

Moments to remember: _____

_____

_____

_____

_____

Success of party / Overall feeling: _____

_____

Tips for next time: _____

_____

_____

Parties

My Entertainment Journal

Notes: _____

_____

_____

_____

_____

_____

_____

_____

_____

_____

_____

_____

_____

Photos

Location: _____ . Date: _____ Time: _____

Hosted by: _____

Guest(s): _____

_____

_____

_____

_____

_____

Occasion / Theme / Event: _____

_____

Foods & Drinks: _____

_____

Music / Entertainment: _____

_____

Gifts / Party favors: _____

_____

Conversations: _____

_____

_____

_____

_____

_____

Moments to remember: _____

_____

_____

_____

_____

Success of party / Overall feeling: _____

_____

Tips for next time: _____

_____

_____

Parties

My Entertainment Journal

Notes: _____

_____

_____

_____

_____

_____

_____

_____

_____

_____

_____

_____

_____

_____

Photos

Location: _____ . Date: _____ Time: _____

Hosted by: _____

Guest(s): _____

_____

_____

_____

_____

Parties

My Entertainment Journal

Occasion / Theme / Event: _____

_____

Foods & Drinks: _____

_____

Music / Entertainment: _____

_____

Gifts / Party favors: _____

_____

Conversations: _____

_____

_____

_____

_____

_____

Moments to remember: _____

_____

_____

_____

_____

Success of party / Overall feeling: _____

_____

Tips for next time: _____

_____

_____

Notes: _____

_____

_____

_____

_____

_____

_____

_____

_____

_____

_____

_____

_____

_____

Photos

Location: _____ . Date: _____ Time: _____

Hosted by: _____

Guest(s): _____

_____

_____

_____

_____

Occasion / Theme / Event: _____

_____

Foods & Drinks: _____

_____

Music / Entertainment: _____

_____

Gifts / Party favors: _____

_____

Conversations: _____

_____

_____

_____

_____

Moments to remember: _____

_____

_____

_____

_____

Success of party / Overall feeling: _____

_____

Tips for next time: _____

_____

_____

Parties

My Entertainment Journal

Notes: _____

_____

_____

_____

_____

_____

_____

_____

_____

_____

_____

_____

_____

_____

Parties

My Entertainment Journal

Photos

Location: _____ Date: _____ Time: _____

Hosted by: _____

Guest(s): _____

_____

_____

_____

_____

Occasion / Theme / Event: _____

_____

Foods & Drinks: _____

_____

Music / Entertainment: _____

_____

Gifts / Party favors: _____

_____

Conversations: _____

_____

_____

_____

_____

Moments to remember: _____

_____

_____

_____

_____

Success of party / Overall feeling: _____

_____

Tips for next time: _____

_____

_____

Parties

My Entertainment Journal

Notes: _____

_____

_____

_____

_____

_____

_____

_____

_____

_____

_____

_____

_____

_____

Parties

My Entertainment Journal

Photos

Location: _____ . Date: _____ Time: _____

Hosted by: _____

Guest(s): _____

_____

_____

_____

_____

Occasion / Theme / Event: _____

_____

Foods & Drinks: _____

_____

Music / Entertainment: _____

_____

Gifts / Party favors: _____

_____

Conversations: _____

_____

_____

_____

_____

Moments to remember: _____

_____

_____

_____

_____

Success of party / Overall feeling: _____

_____

Tips for next time: _____

_____

_____

Parties

My Entertainment Journal

Notes: _____

_____

_____

_____

_____

_____

_____

_____

_____

_____

_____

_____

_____

Photos

Location: _____ Date: _____ Time: _____

Hosted by: _____

Guest(s): _____

_____

_____

_____

_____

Occasion / Theme / Event: _____

_____

Foods & Drinks: _____

_____

Music / Entertainment: _____

_____

Gifts / Party favors: _____

_____

Conversations: _____

_____

_____

_____

_____

Moments to remember: _____

_____

_____

_____

_____

Success of party / Overall feeling: _____

_____

Tips for next time: _____

_____

_____

Notes: _____

_____

_____

_____

_____

_____

_____

_____

_____

_____

_____

_____

_____

_____

_____

Parties

My Entertainment Journal

Photos

Location: _____ . Date: _____ Time: _____

Hosted by: _____

Guest(s): _____

_____

_____

_____

_____

Occasion / Theme / Event: _____

_____

Foods & Drinks: _____

_____

Music / Entertainment: _____

_____

Gifts / Party favors: _____

_____

Conversations: _____

_____

_____

_____

_____

Moments to remember: _____

_____

_____

_____

_____

Success of party / Overall feeling: _____

_____

Tips for next time: _____

_____

_____

Notes: _____

_____

_____

_____

_____

_____

_____

_____

_____

_____

_____

_____

Photos

Location: _____. Date: _____ Time: _____

Hosted by: _____

Guest(s): _____

Parties
My Entertainment Journal

_____

_____

_____

Occasion / Theme / Event: _____

_____

Foods & Drinks: _____

_____

Music / Entertainment: _____

_____

Gifts / Party favors: _____

_____

Conversations: _____

_____

_____

_____

_____

Moments to remember: _____

_____

_____

_____

Success of party / Overall feeling: _____

_____

Tips for next time: _____

_____

Notes: _____

_____

_____

_____

_____

_____

_____

_____

_____

_____

_____

_____

_____

_____

Parties

My Entertainment Journal

Photos

Location: _____ Date: _____ Time: _____

Hosted by: _____

Guest(s): _____

_____

_____

_____

_____

Occasion / Theme / Event: _____

_____

Foods & Drinks: _____

_____

Music / Entertainment: _____

_____

Gifts / Party favors: _____

_____

Conversations: _____

_____

_____

_____

_____

Moments to remember: _____

_____

_____

_____

_____

Success of party / Overall feeling: _____

_____

Tips for next time: _____

_____

_____

Notes: _____

_____

_____

_____

_____

_____

_____

_____

_____

_____

_____

_____

_____

Parties

My Entertainment Journal

Photos

Location: _____ . Date: _____ Time: _____

Hosted by: _____

Guest(s): _____

_____

_____

_____

_____

Occasion / Theme / Event: _____

_____

Foods & Drinks: _____

_____

Music / Entertainment: _____

_____

Gifts / Party favors: _____

_____

Conversations: _____

_____

_____

_____

_____

Moments to remember: _____

_____

_____

_____

_____

Success of party / Overall feeling: _____

_____

Tips for next time: _____

_____

Parties

My Entertainment Journal

Notes: _____

_____

_____

_____

_____

_____

_____

_____

_____

_____

_____

_____

_____

_____

Parties

My Entertainment Journal

Photos

Location: _____. Date: _____ Time: _____

Hosted by: _____

Guest(s): _____

_____

_____

_____

_____

Occasion / Theme / Event: _____

_____

Foods & Drinks: _____

_____

Music / Entertainment: _____

_____

Gifts / Party favors: _____

_____

Conversations: _____

_____

_____

_____

_____

Moments to remember: _____

_____

_____

_____

Success of party / Overall feeling: _____

_____

Tips for next time: _____

_____

_____

Parties

My Entertainment Journal

Notes: _____

_____

_____

_____

_____

_____

_____

_____

_____

_____

_____

_____

_____

_____

Parties

My Entertainment Journal

Photos

Location: _____ . Date: _____ Time: _____

Hosted by: _____

Guest(s): _____

_____

_____

_____

_____

Occasion / Theme / Event: _____

_____

Foods & Drinks: _____

_____

Music / Entertainment: _____

_____

Gifts / Party favors: _____

_____

Conversations: _____

_____

_____

_____

_____

Moments to remember: _____

_____

_____

_____

_____

Success of party / Overall feeling: _____

_____

Tips for next time: _____

_____

_____

Parties

My Entertainment Journal

Notes: _____

_____

_____

_____

_____

_____

_____

_____

_____

_____

_____

_____

Photos

Location: _____ . Date: _____ Time: _____

Hosted by: _____

Guest(s): _____

_____

_____

_____

_____

Occasion / Theme / Event: _____

_____

Foods & Drinks: _____

_____

Music / Entertainment: _____

_____

Gifts / Party favors: _____

_____

Conversations: _____

_____

_____

_____

_____

_____

Moments to remember: _____

_____

_____

_____

_____

Success of party / Overall feeling: _____

_____

Tips for next time: _____

_____

_____

Parties

My Entertainment Journal

Notes: _____

_____

_____

_____

_____

_____

_____

_____

_____

_____

_____

_____

_____

_____

Parties

My Entertainment Journal

Photos

Location: _____ . Date: _____ Time: _____

Hosted by: _____

Guest(s): _____

_____

_____

_____

_____

Occasion / Theme / Event: _____

_____

Foods & Drinks: _____

_____

Music / Entertainment: _____

_____

Gifts / Party favors: _____

_____

Conversations: _____

_____

_____

_____

_____

Moments to remember: _____

_____

_____

_____

Success of party / Overall feeling: _____

_____

Tips for next time: _____

_____

_____

Parties

My Entertainment Journal

Notes: _____
_____
_____
_____
_____
_____
_____
_____
_____
_____
_____
_____
_____

Photos

Location: _____ Date: _____ Time: _____

Hosted by: _____

Guest(s): _____

_____

_____

_____

_____

Occasion / Theme / Event: _____

_____

Foods & Drinks: _____

_____

Music / Entertainment: _____

_____

Gifts / Party favors: _____

_____

Conversations: _____

_____

_____

_____

_____

Moments to remember: _____

_____

_____

_____

_____

Success of party / Overall feeling: _____

_____

Tips for next time: _____

_____

_____

Parties

My Entertainment Journal

Notes: _____

_____

_____

_____

_____

_____

_____

_____

_____

_____

_____

_____

_____

Parties

My Entertainment Journal

Photos

Location: _____ Date: _____ Time: _____

Hosted by: _____

Guest(s): _____

_____

_____

_____

Occasion / Theme / Event: _____

_____

Foods & Drinks: _____

_____

Music / Entertainment: _____

_____

Gifts / Party favors: _____

_____

Conversations: _____

_____

_____

_____

_____

Moments to remember: _____

_____

_____

_____

Success of party / Overall feeling: _____

_____

Tips for next time: _____

_____

_____

Notes: _____

_____

_____

_____

_____

_____

_____

_____

_____

_____

_____

_____

_____

Parties

My Entertainment Journal

Photos

Location: _____ . Date: _____ Time: _____

Hosted by: _____

Guest(s): _____

_____

_____

_____

_____

Occasion / Theme / Event: _____

_____

Foods & Drinks: _____

_____

Music / Entertainment: _____

_____

Gifts / Party favors: _____

_____

Conversations: _____

_____

_____

_____

_____

Moments to remember: _____

_____

_____

_____

Success of party / Overall feeling: _____

_____

Tips for next time: _____

_____

_____

Notes: _____

_____

_____

_____

_____

_____

_____

_____

_____

_____

_____

_____

_____

Photos

Location: _____ . Date: _____ Time: _____

Hosted by: _____

Guest(s): _____

_____

_____

_____

Parties
My Entertainment Journal

Occasion / Theme / Event: _____

_____

Foods & Drinks: _____

_____

Music / Entertainment: _____

_____

Gifts / Party favors: _____

_____

Conversations: _____

_____

_____

_____

_____

Moments to remember: _____

_____

_____

_____

_____

Success of party / Overall feeling: _____

_____

Tips for next time: _____

_____

_____

Notes: _____

Parties
My Entertainment Journal

_____
_____
_____
_____
_____
_____
_____
_____
_____
_____
_____
_____
_____

Photos

Journals Unlimited, Inc.
Our history by Barb Morina - President / Founder

I've always kept a personal journal to express my thoughts, excitement, and concerns and to help me plan and set goals for the future. Everyone experiences important events worth remembering. Whatever your age or passion, keeping a journal is a great way to capture and recall your thoughts and ideas, while recording all your precious memories.

With just an idea, the company was started in the summer of 1997. I was on vacation on the west coast of Michigan when I walked into a Barnes & Noble book store. I wanted a vacation journal and envisioned finding a series of journals with the prompts such as our journals offer (Where I traveled, Where I stayed, People I met, etc.). There was nothing even close, only a wide variety of blank journals. Almost immediately the idea was born!

By the end of the day, I had developed several titles as well as the craft color and cover design. I went to my office the following Monday. At that time I owned and operated a weight-loss franchise in Bay City, Michigan, my hometown. I announced to my store manager that I had come up with a million dollar idea over the weekend, and I was going to put it to work.

I started with just four titles, Vacation, Camping, Golfing, and Boating, and began selling them at craft shows and personally calling on gift stores throughout Michigan. I now have over 100 salespeople representing a continually expanding line with more than 50 titles in various sizes. It has been an empowering ride. The "Write It Down!" Series can be found in retail stores across the USA and Canada. Our most popular title, Me - A Personal Journal, is also printed in Spanish and available in Mexico. In addition to the retail market we also print custom journals for specific client needs.

I owe a great deal to my partner and friend John, as well as friends and family who were always giving me their support and advice. I owe special thanks to Donna Schultz, who serves as my assistant, office manager, and sales manager. The list goes on, for she has worn many other hats. She gave up a comfortable, secure job and joined us in unknown territory to be part of this remarkable journey.

My biggest frustration has been several companies, mostly foreign, that have attempted to make knock offs. Unfortunately, we spend a lot of money on legal fees and dedicate valuable resources to defend our intellectual property rights.

I have been truly blessed with the skill and professionalism of my staff. I was fortunate enough to discover at an early age that the key to success is to surround yourself with people who are smarter and more experienced than you. We are growing with leaps and bounds, and I don't mean just the journals!

I guess what is written on the first page of all my journals sums it up best:
Life is an adventure. It is not the destination we reach that's most rewarding. It's the journey along the way. So Write It Down! and treasure the memory forever...

Barbara Morina